Contents

Choosing a Bike

This extract is from the *Change4Life* website, a health campaign that encourages people to live healthier lifestyles. The website provides tips and ideas to help people eat healthily and to be active. This extract gives advice about choosing the right kind of bike.

Having the right bike makes every trip easier, safer and more fun, and the good news is your bike needn't cost a fortune.

Choosing a bike

5 Think about what you and your family are going to use your bikes for and where you are likely to ride most often. If you are mainly going to ride on tarmac, the bike you need will be different to if you are going to be riding on muddy tracks.

Here's a list of the most popular types of bike and the sorts of cycling they're suitable for:

10 ### Mountain bike
These are great all-round bikes as they are good on the road and even better on rough tracks. They often have knobbly tyres for extra grip and suspension to cushion the bumps. You can also add things like mudguards and a carrier rack on many models, so they're practical too!

15 ### Hybrid bike
A cross between a road bike and a cross-country mountain bike, taking the most popular bits from both. It often has things like suspension in the seat and bigger wheels to make it very comfortable. A great bike for beginners and riders using tarmac roads most of the time.

20 ### Racing bike
A streamlined bike with very thin tyres and drop handlebars for fast riding on the road. It can be made of very light materials and have a saddle that's only really comfortable if you're wearing special cycling clothes. A bike that's best for experienced cyclists.

From *www.nhs.uk/change4life*

1 Write down one advantage of having the right type of bike.

....

1 mark

2 Why are mountain bikes described as "great all-round bikes" (line 11)?

....

1 mark

3 What does "hybrid" in line 15 mean? Use a dictionary to help you.
Why is this a suitable name for this type of bike?

....

....

2 marks

4 How are hybrid bikes like mountain bikes?

....

1 mark

5 Why would you need suspension on a mountain bike but not on a racing bike?

....

....

1 mark

6 Which type of bike owner is most likely to benefit from padded shorts and why?

....

....

2 marks

7 Which type of bike would you choose? Explain your answer.

....

2 marks

....

Total
out of 10

....

The Tale of Custard the Dragon

This poem was written by Ogden Nash, who is known for his funny poems. It is about a girl called Belinda who lives with her four pets: a kitten, a mouse, a dog and a dragon. The dragon is teased by the others for being cowardly, but one day, he proves that he *can* be brave...

The Tale of Custard the Dragon

Belinda lived in a little white house,
With a little black kitten and a little gray mouse,
And a little yellow dog and a little red wagon,
And a realio, trulio, little pet dragon.

5 Now the name of the little black kitten was Ink,
And the little gray mouse, she called her Blink,
And the little yellow dog was sharp as Mustard,
But the dragon was a coward, and she called him Custard.

Custard the dragon had big sharp teeth,
10 And spikes on top of him and scales underneath,
Mouth like a fireplace, chimney for a nose,
And realio, trulio, daggers on his toes.

Belinda was as brave as a barrel full of bears,
And Ink and Blink chased lions down the stairs,
15 Mustard was as brave as a tiger in a rage,
But Custard cried for a nice safe cage.

Belinda tickled him, she tickled him unmerciful,
Ink, Blink and Mustard, they rudely called him Percival,
They all sat laughing in the little red wagon
20 At the realio, trulio, cowardly dragon.

Belinda giggled till she shook the house,
And Blink said Week!, which is giggling for a mouse,
Ink and Mustard rudely asked his age,
When Custard cried for a nice safe cage.

25 Suddenly, suddenly they heard a nasty sound,
And Mustard growled, and they all looked around.
Meowch! cried Ink, and Ooh! cried Belinda,
For there was a pirate, climbing in the winda.

Pistol in his left hand, pistol in his right,
30 And he held in his teeth a cutlass bright,
His beard was black, one leg was wood;
It was clear that the pirate meant no good.

Belinda paled, and she cried, Help! Help!
But Mustard fled with a terrified yelp,
35 Ink trickled down to the bottom of the household,
And little mouse Blink strategically mouseholed.

But up jumped Custard, snorting like an engine,
Clashed his tail like irons in a dungeon,
With a clatter and a clank and a jangling squirm
40 He went at the pirate like a robin at a worm.

The pirate gaped at Belinda's dragon,
And gulped some grog from his pocket flagon,
He fired two bullets but they didn't hit,
And Custard gobbled him, every bit.

45 Belinda embraced him, Mustard licked him,
No one mourned for his pirate victim
Ink and Blink in glee did gyrate
Around the dragon that ate the pyrate.

Belinda still lives in her little white house,
50 With her little black kitten and her little gray mouse,
And her little yellow dog and her little red wagon,
And her realio, trulio, little pet dragon.

Belinda is as brave as a barrel full of bears,
And Ink and Blink chase lions down the stairs,
55 Mustard is as brave as a tiger in a rage,
But Custard keeps crying for a nice safe cage.

Ogden Nash

(1) **Why do you think Belinda calls her kitten 'Ink'?**

....

1 mark

(2) **Summarise how Custard the Dragon looks in the third verse.**

....

....

....

2 marks

(3) **Why do you think the poet compares the dragon's mouth to a fireplace in line 11?**

....

1 mark

(4) **Why do you think the poet has spelt the word 'window' differently in line 28?**

....

1 mark

(5) **Why does Belinda's face pale in line 33?**

....

1 mark

(6) **What does "embraced" mean in line 45? Use a dictionary to help you. What does this show about Belinda's feelings towards Custard?**

....

....

2 marks

(7) **How do you think Custard feels after fighting the pirate?**

....

2 marks

....

Total
out of 10

....

Aesop's Fables

Aesop's Fables are a collection of short stories said to have been told by Aesop, a slave in Ancient Greece. These stories have been passed down for generations, and each one contains a message, known as a moral, which teaches the reader a lesson about how to live their life.

The Fox and the Stork

The Fox one day thought of a plan to amuse himself at the expense of the Stork, at whose odd appearance he was always laughing.

"You must come and dine with me today," he said to the Stork, smiling to himself at the trick he was going to play. The Stork gladly accepted the invitation and arrived in good time and with a
5   very good appetite.

For dinner the Fox served soup. But it was set out in a very shallow dish, and all the Stork could do was to wet the very tip of his bill. Not a drop of soup could he get. But the Fox lapped it up easily, and, to increase the disappointment of the Stork, made a great show of enjoyment.

The hungry Stork was much displeased at the trick, but he was a calm, even-tempered fellow
10   and saw no good in flying into a rage. Instead, not long afterward, he invited the Fox to dine with him in turn. The Fox arrived promptly at the time that had been set, and the Stork served a fish dinner that had a very appetizing smell. But it was served in a tall jar with a very narrow neck. The Stork could easily get at the food with his long bill, but all the Fox could do was to lick the outside of the jar, and sniff at the delicious odor. And when the Fox lost his temper, the Stork said calmly:

15   *Do not play tricks on your neighbors unless you can stand the same treatment yourself.*

The Fox and the Crow

One bright morning as the Fox was following his sharp nose through the wood in search of a bite to eat, he saw a Crow on the limb of a tree overhead. This was by no means the first Crow the Fox had ever seen. What caught his attention this time and made him stop for
5   a second look, was that the lucky Crow held a bit of cheese in her beak.

"No need to search any farther," thought sly Master Fox. "Here is a dainty bite for my breakfast."

Up he trotted to the foot of the tree in which the Crow was sitting, and looking up
10   admiringly, he cried, "Good-morning, beautiful creature!"

The Crow, her head cocked on one side, watched the Fox suspiciously. But she kept her beak tightly closed on the cheese and did not return his greeting.

"What a charming creature she is!" said the Fox. "How her feathers shine! What a beautiful form and what splendid wings! Such a wonderful Bird should have a very lovely voice,
15   since everything else about her is so perfect. Could she sing just one song, I know I should hail her Queen of Birds."

Listening to these flattering words, the Crow forgot all her suspicion, and also her breakfast. She wanted very much to be called Queen of Birds.

So she opened her beak wide to utter her loudest caw,
20   and down fell the cheese straight into the Fox's open mouth.

"Thank you," said Master Fox sweetly, as he walked off. "Though it is cracked, you have a voice sure enough. But where are your wits?"

1 In your own words, explain why the Fox invites the Stork round for dinner in *The Fox and the Stork?*

....

1 mark

2 Why doesn't the Stork get angry when the Fox plays a trick on him?

....

1 mark

3 How does the Stork teach the Fox a lesson in *The Fox and the Stork?*

....

....

....

2 marks

4 What does the word "sly" mean in line 7 of *The Fox and the Crow?* What is the Fox doing that is sly?

....

....

2 marks

5 Why do you think the Crow "forgot all her suspicion" (line 17) about the Fox?

....

....

1 mark

6 A moral is a lesson that can be learnt from a story. What do you think the moral is of *The Fox and the Crow?*

....

1 mark

7 Why do you think a fox was chosen for both fables?

....

2 marks

....

Total out of 10

....

An Interview with Jacqueline Wilson

Jacqueline Wilson is a popular children's author who has written many novels. Some of her best-known books include the *Tracy Beaker* series, which was also made into a television programme, and *The Illustrated Mum*. This extract is from an interview with the author.

How old were you when your first book you wrote was published?

I was writing stories throughout my childhood, and my first short story was published when I was 17. But I was 22 before I got a book published.

How did you first become interested in writing? Did any author or teacher inspire you?

5   I loved books, I liked pictures, and it evolved from there. No, at my primary school, they made a fuss of me, I was chosen to read my stories aloud. At secondary school, stories were made to be more formal, so I had lots of corrections. So I feel if they read any of my books now I'd still get full of red marks! Do it the school way at school and your own way at home.

How long have you been writing books? And what is your favourite book you have written?

10   I never can decide, I think it's possibly *The Illustrated Mum*, it's probably the saddest of my stories, but it came almost how I wanted it to be. Each time I start a book, I want it to be this and that and it hardly ever does. I've written over 100 books now.

How do you come up with all your ideas?

I think it's a bit like asking you, where you get your dreams from, you don't exactly know, do you?
15   Dreams are distorted and you have no idea where they came from. I don't know what's going to come next! I came up for the name of Tracy Beaker in my bath. I knew I wanted her to be called Tracy and be a feisty girl but I couldn't think of the right surname for her. In my bath, I came up with Tracy Toilet, Tracy Bath and lots more and then I was washing my hair and I pulled up this beaker to wash my hair down with, and that's when it came to me "Tracy Beaker".

20   **Did you ever think your books would become a TV series?**

No I didn't. For years and years, I got letters from children saying why don't you make such and such a TV Show? I was thrilled to bits with *Tracy Beaker*. I met a lovely woman called Sue, who held on to that idea for years and I don't know how anyone thought it would be that big. I do like to visit the set, I don't write the script as there's too many and it wouldn't be possible. They've
25   written it just the way I would have though!

How long does it take to write a book?

It takes too long! Children read them in 3 days and think it takes that long to write it – I wish it did. I write little bits on the train, and here and there. I try to write at least 500 words a day, then when it's finished I type it up, it can take as long as 6 months. I like to get two books written a year.

From *https://clubs-kids.scholastic.co.uk*

1 How old was Jacqueline Wilson when her first book was published?

....

1 mark

2 Why do you think she had "lots of corrections" in her stories at secondary school?

....

1 mark

3 Why is *The Illustrated Mum* Jacqueline Wilson's favourite book?

....

1 mark

4 Why does she compare her ideas to dreams?

....

....

....

2 marks

5 In your own words, explain how Jacqueline Wilson came up with Tracy Beaker's surname.

....

....

1 mark

6 Why do you think she was "thrilled to bits" (line 22)
when *Tracy Beaker* was made into a TV series?

....

....

2 marks

7 What do you think it would be like to be such a popular author? Explain your answer.

....

2 marks

....

Total
out of 10

....

Harry Drinkwater's Diary

Harry Drinkwater was a soldier who fought in World War One (1914-1918). He joined the army at the outbreak of war and served until the war ended. He kept a diary throughout the war, which has now been published as a book. The text below is an extract from his diary.

<u>Monday, December 20, 1915</u>
The trenches are in a terrible condition — anything up to 4ft deep in mud and water. We're plastered in mud up to our faces. Our food — cold bacon, bread and jam — is slung together in a sack that hangs from the dripping dugout roof. Consequently, we eat and drink mud.

5 <u>Saturday, March 4, 1916</u>
Nothing here but trench after trench and, in places, the ground blown into heaps of dirt. The trees have been hacked to pieces — only black stumps remain. Nothing grows. Utter desolation.

<u>Tuesday, March 7</u>
Worked at a feverish pace, digging and strengthening trenches all through last night. Then
10 through the day, I have to do an hour's sentry duty* every third hour. This is followed by an hour as the relief man, when I'm able to sit down. For the third hour, I can sleep. I'm feeling like most of the other fellows — half dead.

<u>Thursday, March 9</u>
Owing to food transports going astray, we have one loaf between five of us, a few biscuits and
15 half a tin of marmalade each per day. Have just heard we have a ten-mile march before we can be billeted* [for rest]. Jolly hard lines.

<u>Friday, March 10</u>
It was snowing as we set out at 11.15 last night. I saw two fellows — fast asleep as they walked along — walk out of the ranks and fall into the ditch at the side of the road. We halted for ten
20 minutes' rest and I dropped down into a puddle and went to sleep. Was unable to get up without help, and ended up hanging on to Lieutenant Davis on one side and a stretcher-bearer the other. Tried to pull myself together and went headlong on the road. They got me to my feet again but I was helpless. Have a vague idea that I was laid on some straw. Then oblivion.

<u>Sunday, May 7</u>
25 Working in the mines — an awful strain mentally. We're some three-parts of a mile under the ground. Air is got down by means of a large pair of blacksmith's bellows*, connected to a long pipe. But it's very stuffy, and we work with backs bent for eight hours.

An extract from *Harry's War* by Harry Drinkwater.

	<u>Glossary</u>	
sentry duty — keeping guard	blacksmith's bellows — a tool which gives out air	
billeted — housed		

1 Why do you think the trenches are full of water?

....
1 mark

2 Why do the soldiers "eat and drink mud" in line 4?

....
1 mark

3 What does "feverish" in line 9 mean? Use a dictionary to help you.
What does this word tell you about how the soldiers worked?

....

....
2 marks

4 Why do you think Harry feels "half dead" in line 12?

....

....
1 mark

5 Why did the soldiers have so little food?

....
1 mark

6 What happened to Harry on Friday, March 10?

....

....
2 marks

7 Why do you think that working in the mines was "an awful strain mentally" (line 25)?

....
2 marks

....

....
Total
out of 10

Hamish and the Worldstoppers

Hamish and the Worldstoppers is by Danny Wallace. It is about a boy called Hamish, who one day realises that he can do whatever he likes when everything in the world stops, except for him. In this extract, Hamish is in school when he realises that something very strange is happening...

Hamish Ellerby's eyes were the size of satsumas as he sat completely still in his chair.

And he sat completely still because he was totally, utterly petrified.

This was so strange.

5 What on earth was going on?

Seriously – what on *earth*?

It had all happened in an instant. The scariest, coolest, most awful, most brilliant, most horrible, most wonderful thing.

Hamish wanted to get up and look around. But he couldn't. He was
10 too frightened even to move a single muscle.

This was *incredi*-weird!

Just a matter of moments ago, gangly Mr Longblather had been leaning forward onto a desk using just his knuckles, the way he always did when he was about to ask Class 4E of Winterbourne School a question.

15 "Who can tell me about soil erosion?" he'd said, and everybody's hearts had sunk at once, because if there's anything more boring than soil erosion then no one's told me about it. Mr Longblather was one of those particularly boring teachers, with a particular talent for making particularly boring things even more particularly boring than normal. In
20 this respect, at least, Mr Longblather was absolutely extraordinary.

When the question had been asked, Hamish had stared down at his pencil case and made his special *ooh-let-me-think* face. He ran his hand through the thick black hair his mum called 'The Mess' and squeezed his huge greeny-brown eyes shut, like he was really trying to come up with an
25 answer. Sometimes he found this was enough to convince people he was thinking about soil erosion. (Fact: Hamish had never really thought about soil erosion. It was not something he was all that concerned about. To be honest, he didn't even really know what soil erosion was.)

An extract from *Hamish and the Worldstoppers* by Danny Wallace.

1   Why are Hamish's eyes described as "the size of satsumas" in line 1?

....

1 mark

2   Why do you think the words "seriously" and "earth" in line 6 are in italics?

....

1 mark

3   Write down one negative and one positive adjective
that Hamish uses to describe what's happening.

....

1 mark

4   Which two words is *"incredi*-weird" (line 11) made from? What do you think it means?

....

....

2 marks

5   What does "blather" mean? Use a dictionary to help you. Why do you
think the author chose to name Hamish's teacher "Mr Longblather"?

....

....

....

2 marks

6   Read the introduction to the extract. What do you think has happened in the extract?

....

1 mark

7   Did the last paragraph of the extract make you want to keep reading?
Explain your answer.

....

2 marks

....

Total
out of 10

....

BBC Women's Footballer of the Year

The *BBC Women's Footballer of the Year* award was introduced in 2015. The winner is voted for by members of the public. In 2015, five players were short-listed for the award and Asisat Oshoala was chosen as the winner. This article describes her reaction to winning.

Asisat Oshoala named first BBC Women's Footballer of the Year

Liverpool footballer Asisat Oshoala has become the first player to win the BBC Women's Footballer of the Year. The 20-year-old forward, who also plays for
5 Nigeria, was voted for by football fans around the world.

Oshoala said the award had left her feeling 'happy and appreciated'.

She said: "I would like to say thank you
10 to the BBC, to my fans around the world and to everyone who voted. It's a very good thing for me and also motivation for the World Cup. I had a very good 2014 and had the opportunity of going to
15 the under-20s Women's World Cup with Nigeria and also won the Golden Ball and Golden Boot so I think maybe that added to the reason why people voted for me."
[...]
Oshoala signed for Liverpool Ladies in
20 January 2015, with Manager Matt Beard calling her "one of the world's top young footballers".

She is the first African to feature in the Women's Super League, and says former

25 Reds striker Luis Suarez is an inspiration because of his ruthlessness in front of goal.
[...]
Mary Hockaday, Controller of BBC World Service English, said: "Huge congratulations to Asisat Oshoala on winning the first
30 BBC Women's Footballer of the Year award. At still only 20, she's proved herself a formidable talent on the pitch. I'm proud BBC World Service is supporting the women's game and thrilled with the
35 interest in the award. I look forward to seeing who comes through in next year's shortlist."

The youngest footballer to be shortlisted, Oshoala played at the Under-20 World
40 Cup in Canada last summer where she was the tournament's leading scorer and voted best player.

Her performances led Nigeria to the final, where they were narrowly beaten
45 by Germany. Oshoala was also a major influence in the senior Nigeria team, who won the African Women's Championship later in 2014, ensuring their qualification for this summer's World Cup.

An abridged article from *www.prolificnorth.co.uk*

1 Why does Oshoala feel "appreciated" (line 8)?

....

....

1 mark

2 Why do you think winning the award is "motivation for the World Cup" (lines 12-13)?

....

....

1 mark

3 In your own words, explain why Oshoala thinks people voted for her.

....

....

1 mark

4 Mary Hockaday describes Oshoala as "a formidable talent" (line 32). What does this phrase mean? Use a dictionary to help you.

....

1 mark

5 Which two adjectives does Mary Hockaday use to describe her feelings about the award?

....

2 marks

6 How did Oshoala perform at the Under-20 World Cup in Canada? Find examples from the text to support your answer.

....

....

2 marks

7 Do you think it was a good idea for the BBC to introduce this award? Explain your answer.

....

....

2 marks

....

Total
out of 10

....

The Real Princess

Hans Christian Andersen was a Danish author. He is best known for his fairy tales such as *The Ugly Duckling*, *The Little Mermaid* and *The Snow Queen*. *The Real Princess* tells the story of a prince who wants to marry a real princess, but isn't having much luck finding one...

There was once a prince who wanted to marry a princess. But she must be a real princess, mind you. So he travelled all round the world, seeking such a one, but everywhere something was in the way. Not that there was any lack of princesses, but he could not seem to make out whether they were real princesses; there was
5   always something not quite satisfactory. Therefore, home he came again, quite out of spirits, for he wished so much to marry a real princess.

One evening a terrible storm came on. It thundered and lightened, and the rain poured down; indeed, it was quite fearful. In the midst of it there came a knock at the town gate, and the old king went out to open it.
10   It was a princess who stood outside. But O dear, what a state she was in from the rain and bad weather! The water dropped from her hair and clothes, it ran in at the tips of her shoes and out at the heels; yet she insisted she was a real princess.

"Very well," thought the old queen; "that we shall presently see." She said nothing, but went into the bedchamber and took off all the bedding, then laid a pea
15   on the sacking of the bedstead*. Having done this, she took twenty mattresses and laid them upon the pea and placed twenty eider-down* beds on top of the mattresses.

The princess lay upon this bed all the night. In the morning she was asked how she had slept.

"Oh, most miserably!" she said. "I scarcely closed my eyes the whole night
20   through. I cannot think what there could have been in the bed. I lay upon something so hard that I am quite black and blue all over. It is dreadful!"

It was now quite evident that she was a real princess, since through twenty mattresses and twenty eider-down beds she had felt the pea. None but a real princess could have such delicate feeling.
25   So the prince took her for his wife, for he knew that in her he had found a true princess. And the pea was preserved in the cabinet of curiosities, where it is still to be seen unless someone has stolen it.

And this, mind you, is a real story.

An extract from *The Real Princess* by Hans Christian Andersen.

> **Glossary**
>
> bedstead — the frame of a bed
>
> eider-down — duck feathers used to stuff bedding

1 What does "out of spirits" in lines 5-6 mean? Why does the prince feel like this?

....

....

2 marks

2 Why do you think the princess knocks on the town gate?

....

1 mark

3 Why does the queen put so much bedding on the bed, but say "nothing" about what she has done?

....

....

....

2 marks

4 What does the princess mean when she says she is "black and blue all over" (line 21)?

....

1 mark

5 How do you think the prince feels when he finds out that the princess felt the pea under all of the bedding? Explain your answer.

....

....

2 marks

6 Why do you think the royal family preserved the pea?

....

2 marks

....

....

Total
out of 10

© Not to be photocopied

Year 4 — Targeted Comprehension

Chinese New Year

Chinese New Year is an important festival in the Chinese calendar. It is a time when family and friends get together to welcome in the new year. In this text, you'll find out all about Chinese New Year, and about the Chinese calendar, which is different from the Western calendar.

Chinese New Year is the biggest and most important celebration for Chinese people. The festival lasts for fifteen days. The date of Chinese New Year changes every year, but the first day of the festival is always between 21st January and 20th February.

5 The Chinese calendar is organised in a twelve-year cycle. Each year is named after an animal, and people are said to have similar characteristics to the animal associated with their birth year.

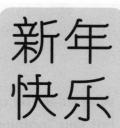

新年
快乐

"Happy New Year"
in Mandarin Chinese

Rat — 2008, 1996, 1984, 1972, 1960
Charming, quick-witted and full of energy, rats
10 work hard and have ambition, but they can be
selfish and greedy.

Ox — 2009, 1997, 1985, 1973, 1961
Oxen are reliable and hard-working, and their
honesty and loyalty are valued. They are usually
15 quiet, but can be stubborn.

Tiger — 2010, 1998, 1986, 1974, 1962
Brave, enthusiastic, passionate and confident,
tigers are born leaders. However, they can
sometimes be unpredictable and disobedient.

20 **Rabbit — 2011, 1999, 1987, 1975, 1963**
Rabbits are gentle and compassionate, and
prefer peace to conflict. They often tend to be
insecure and cautious.

Dragon — 2012, 2000, 1988, 1976, 1964
25 Dragons are confident, ambitious and successful,
but can be aggressive and arrogant. The dragon
is an important Chinese cultural symbol, so
Chinese people consider it a very lucky year.

Snake — 2013, 2001, 1989, 1977, 1965
30 Snakes are wise but mysterious. They think a
lot and are usually financially successful, but can
be dishonest and judgemental.

Horse — 2014, 2002, 1990, 1978, 1966
Energetic and talented, horses are very popular
35 and like to be the centre of attention. They have
a tendency to be self-centred.

Goat — 2015, 2003, 1991, 1979, 1967
Goats are creative, gentle and clever, and are
tougher than others think. However, they often
40 worry and can be pessimistic and insecure.

Monkey — 2016, 2004, 1992, 1980, 1968
Monkeys are adventurous and mischievous.
They are lively, sociable and find it hard to relax.
They can often be cunning.

45 **Rooster — 2017, 2005, 1993, 1981, 1969**
Roosters are motivated, organised and
independent. They're straightforward, but often
outspoken and a little vain.

Dog — 2018, 2006, 1994, 1982, 1970
50 Loyal and honest, dogs have a strong sense of
justice and fairness. They can, however, worry
unnecessarily and be bad-tempered.

Pig — 2019, 2007, 1995, 1983, 1971
Generous and modest, with a loving and caring
55 nature, pigs like to see the good in people, but
can sometimes be too trusting.

Written by Alex Fairer.

1 If the first day of Chinese New Year falls on 8ᵗʰ February, what is the date of the last day of the festival?

.... 1 mark

2 Which animal sign is good at being in charge, according to the text?

.... 1 mark

3 What does "compassionate" (line 21) mean? Use a dictionary to help you. Why do you think this is seen as a positive quality?

....
.... 2 marks

4 Which animal sign do you think is the most desirable for Chinese people? Why?

....
.... 2 marks

5 Which animal sign does the text suggest is the most artistic?

.... 1 mark

6 Which year comes after the year of the pig?

.... 1 mark

7 Do the characteristics of the animal for the year you were born in reflect your personality? Explain your answer.

.... 2 marks

.... **Total** out of 10

....

The Girl Who Walked On Air

The Girl Who Walked On Air is written by Emma Carroll, an author and English teacher.
It is about a girl called Louie who works in the ticket office of a circus, but dreams about
performing in the circus herself. In this extract, she can't wait to see an evening performance...

The bigger the danger, the bigger the crowd.
One look at tonight's punters said it all. With just
minutes till show time, the big top was almost full
and I was quite ready to burn with excitement.
5   Every last ticket was sold. And still the queue
snaked out of the field and down the lane until all
you could see were people's hats bobbing above
the hedgerows.

First thing this morning, the posters had gone up
10   all over town. 'MORE DARING THAN EVER!' they'd said in blue and gold letters.
'WATCH MONSIEUR MERCURY DEFY GRAVITY ON HIS TRAPEZE!' To me,
M. Mercury was good old Jasper, who I lived with in a tiny trailer, and who drank lapsang
tea* out of dainty cups and let me have first dibs on every piecrust. Which was more than
could be said for my mam. When I was just a baby she left me at the circus, the way most
15   people forget an umbrella.

Inside the ticket booth where I worked there wasn't space to swing a cat. I felt
it specially tonight, jiggling from foot to foot, impatient to get finished so I'd be free to
watch the show. My dog Pip sensed it too; sat beside me, he watched my every move. At
last, the final punters filed past to claim their tickets. They were a noisy bunch, laughing
20   and nattering, their breath like smoke in the evening air. They'd be quiet soon enough.
Once they were inside the big top, they'd squeeze onto a bench and look upwards. And
what they'd see would leave them speechless.

A little shiver went down my neck. *Imagine if I was about to perform. All those
eyes gazing up at me. Just imagine it!*
25   I came back to earth with a bump. The circus owner, Mr Leo Chipchase, was in the
doorway. He'd put on his best tartan waistcoat and was smiling, which made a change.

'Think of all those backsides on seats, Louie,' he said as he squeezed in
beside me to count the takings. 'The bigger the danger...'

'...the bigger the crowd,' I finished for him.
30   He did have a point. There were grander circuses than ours, with more animals,
more curiosities, more sparkle. Backsides on seats mattered. So, what better way to draw
the crowds than a thrilling new routine. And tonight that's exactly what they'd get. Jasper
would perform not a double but a TRIPLE somersault from his trapeze. No other circus
boasted such a stunt. It was genius.

An extract from *The Girl Who Walked On Air* by Emma Carroll.

Glossary
lapsang tea — a type of black tea with a smoky flavour

1 Why do you think the crowds are bigger when there is more danger?

....

....

1 mark

2 Jasper lets Louie "have first dibs on every piecrust" (line 13).
What does this suggest about Jasper's personality? Explain your answer.

....

....

2 marks

3 How do you think Louie feels about her mother? Explain your answer.

....

....

2 marks

4 Why are lines 23-24 in italics?

....

1 mark

5 The extract says that although Leo Chipchase didn't smile very often,
he "was smiling" (line 26). Why do you think this is?

....

....

1 mark

6 Why is Jasper's triple somersault stunt described as "genius" in line 34?

....

....

1 mark

7 After reading the title of the book and this extract, explain
what you think might happen in the rest of the book.

....

2 marks

....

Total
out of 10

....

Reign of the Sea Dragons

Reign of the Sea Dragons is an information book by Sneed Collard about reptiles known as "sea dragons" — creatures that lived in the oceans at the same time as dinosaurs lived on Earth. This extract introduces sea dragons and how they were different from today's ocean creatures.

In a time when dinosaurs walked the earth, a strange, large animal called an *elasmosaur* (ee-LAZ-moh-sohr) slipped silently through warm ocean waters.

5   The elasmosaur had long, elegant flippers to propel its turtle-shaped body, and a fifteen-foot neck that came in handy for sneaking up on its favorite food, squid. Soon, in fact, the elasmosaur spotted a school of squid and began swimming toward

10   it. As it opened its jaws to strike, however, a thirty-foot-long *pliosaur* (PLEE-oh-sohr) suddenly shot up out of the depths. With its massive, seven-foot long jaws, the pliosaur seized the elasmosaur and impaled it with dozens of cone-shaped teeth. The elasmosaur struggled and thrashed to free itself, but it was no use. Soon, it died and became prey in the *food web* of the ancient ocean world.

15 <u>Radical Reptiles</u>

The elasmosaur and the pliosaur belonged to an astonishing collection of reptiles that filled our oceans during the *Mesozoic* (MEZ-oh-zoh-ik) era, about 250 to 65 million years ago. Some of these reptiles, such as crocodilians and turtles, have familiar relatives that survive today. Most, however, were totally different from anything in our modern world.

20 They included porpoiselike *ichthyosaurs* (IK-thee-oh-sohrs), the long-necked elasmosaurs, and enormous *mosasaurs* (MOSS-uh-sohrs) with curved daggers for teeth. Scientists often refer to these reptiles as sea dragons, and they include some of the most extraordinary, awesome predators the world has ever known.

An extract from *Reign of the Sea Dragons* by Sneed Collard.

1 What is the purpose of the words in brackets?

....

1 mark

2 What does the word "propel" (line 6) mean? Use a dictionary to help you.

....

1 mark

3 Describe one feature of the elasmosaur and one feature of the pliosaur that helped them catch prey.

....

....

2 marks

4 Name one thing that the elasmosaur liked to eat.

....

1 mark

5 Who eats who in "the *food web* of the ancient ocean world" (line 14)?

....

1 mark

6 Which creature is both predator and prey in this extract?

....

1 mark

7 Why does the author say that mosasaurs had "curved daggers for teeth" (line 21)?

....

....

1 mark

8 Why do you think some scientists call the types of creature mentioned in the extract "sea dragons"?

....

2 marks

....

Total
out of 10

Peter Pan

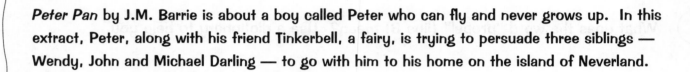

Peter Pan by J.M. Barrie is about a boy called Peter who can fly and never grows up. In this extract, Peter, along with his friend Tinkerbell, a fairy, is trying to persuade three siblings — Wendy, John and Michael Darling — to go with him to his home on the island of Neverland.

They were all on their beds, and gallant* Michael let go first. He did not quite mean to let go, but he did it, and immediately he was borne* across the room.

"I flewed!" he screamed while still in mid-air.

John let go and met Wendy near the bathroom.

5   "Oh, lovely!"

"Oh, ripping!"

"Look at me!"

"Look at me!"

"Look at me!"

10   They were not nearly so elegant as Peter, they could not help kicking a little, but their heads were bobbing against the ceiling, and there is almost nothing so delicious as that. Peter gave Wendy a hand at first, but had to desist*, Tink was so indignant*.

Up and down they went, and round and round. Heavenly was Wendy's word.

"I say," cried John, "why shouldn't we all go out?"

15   Of course it was to this that Peter had been luring* them.

Michael was ready: he wanted to see how long it took him to do a billion miles. But Wendy hesitated.

"Mermaids!" said Peter again.

"Oo!"

20   "And there are pirates."

"Pirates," cried John, seizing his Sunday hat, "let us go at once."

It was just at this moment that Mr. and Mrs. Darling hurried with Nana out of 27. They ran into the middle of the street to look up at the nursery window; and, yes, it was still shut, but the room was ablaze with light, and most heart-gripping sight of all,

25   they could see in shadow on the curtain three little figures in night attire* circling round and round, not on the floor but in the air.

Not three figures, four!

An extract from *Peter Pan* by J.M. Barrie.

Glossary		
gallant — brave	desist — stop	luring — attracting
borne — carried	indignant — annoyed	attire — clothes

1 What happens to Michael in lines 1-2?

....

1 mark

2 Who is better at flying, Peter or the other children? How can you tell?

....

....

2 marks

3 Which adjective does Wendy use to describe flying in lines 10-15?

....

1 mark

4 Why do you think Wendy hesitates in line 17?

....

1 mark

5 How does Peter try to tempt the three children to go with him?

....

1 mark

6 How do you think the children's parents, Mr and Mrs Darling, are feeling in lines 22-27? Explain your answer.

....

....

2 marks

7 In *Peter Pan*, Peter never grows up. Do you want to grow up, or would you like to be a child forever? Explain your answer.

....

2 marks

....

Total
out of 10

....

Bletchley Park Codebreakers

Bletchley Park is in Buckinghamshire, England. During World War Two, people worked there to break German codes which allowed them to read secret German messages. This extract shows how a crossword in *The Daily Telegraph* helped recruit codebreakers to work at Bletchley.

Could you have been a codebreaker at Bletchley Park?

The Daily Telegraph's cryptic crossword on January 13 1942 played a crucial role in helping the Allies win the Second World War.

5　In January 1942, a series of letters to The Daily Telegraph had claimed that the paper's crossword wasn't hard enough. It could be solved in a matter of minutes, they said; so a man
10　called WAJ Gavin, the chairman of the Eccentric Club, suggested this be put to the test. He put up a £100 prize, to be donated to charity in the event that anyone could do it, and Arthur Watson,
15　the paper's then editor, arranged a competition in the newsroom on Fleet Street.

　　Five people beat the 12-minute deadline, although one, the fastest, had
20　misspelled a word and was disqualified. The puzzle was printed in the next day's edition, January 13 1942, so that everyone could try their hand. And there the matter might have rested

25　– but, unknown to the Telegraph and the contestants, the War Office was watching. Stanley Sedgewick, one of those who took part, said: "Several weeks later, I received a letter
30　marked 'Confidential' inviting me, as a consequence of taking part in 'The Daily Telegraph Crossword Time Test', to make an appointment to see Col Nichols of the General Staff, who
35　'would very much like to see you on a matter of national importance'." Mr Sedgewick, and several others who took part that day, ended up working at Bletchley Park, breaking German
40　military codes.

　　[...]

　　Crosswords are about getting inside the mind of your opponent, and in the same way, codebreaking was about getting inside the mind of your enemy. The
45　codebreakers came to know the people encoding the messages individually, by their styles, as crossword-solvers come to know setters. One, Mavis Batey, worked out that two of the Enigma
50　machine operators had girlfriends called Rosa: "She worked it out, trying different options, like in a crossword. Once it worked once, it was an obvious option elsewhere."

An abridged article from *www.telegraph.co.uk*

1 What is different about the presentation of lines 1-4? Why do you think this is?

....
....

2 marks

2 What was WAJ Gavin's idea?

....
....

1 mark

3 Why was the War Office interested in the competition?

....
....

1 mark

4 What does "confidential" (line 30) mean? Use a dictionary to help you.
Why do you think this word was written on the letter to Stanley Sedgewick?

....
....

2 marks

5 According to the article, how are codebreaking and solving crosswords similar?

....
....

1 mark

6 How did *The Daily Telegraph's* cryptic crossword
help the Allies win the Second World War?

....
....

1 mark

7 How do you think you would have felt if you had been asked to be a codebreaker
in the war after completing a newspaper crossword? Explain your answer.

....

2 marks

....

Total
out of 10

....

Poems about Witches

The Witch by Percy H. Ilott and *Two Witches* by Alexander Resnikoff are both poems about witches. They are popular poems which are often used in poetry collections. In *The Witch*, the narrator gets a surprise, and *Two Witches* is about two witches with a bit of a problem...

The Witch

I saw her plucking cowslips*,
And marked her where she stood:
She never knew I watched her
While hiding in the wood.

5   Her skirt was brightest crimson,
And black her steeple hat*,
Her broomstick lay beside her—
I'm positive of that.

Her chin was sharp and pointed,
10   Her eyes were—I don't know—
For, when she turned towards me—
I thought it best—to go!

Percy H. Ilott

Glossary

cowslips — a type of flower

steeple hat — a cone-shaped hat

Two Witches

There was a witch
The witch had an itch
The itch was so itchy it
Gave her a twitch.

5   Another witch
Admired the twitch
So she started twitching
Though she had no itch.

Now both of them twitch
10   So it's hard to tell which
Witch has the itch and
Which witch has the twitch.

Alexander Resnikoff

(1) **Why do you think the witch was picking cowslips in *The Witch*?**

....
1 mark

(2) **What colour is the witch's skirt in *The Witch*? Circle one.**

a. black   b. blue   c. red   d. orange
1 mark

(3) **Why do you think the narrator decided to leave at the end of *The Witch*?**

....

....
1 mark

(4) **Why is it hard to tell which witch has the itch in *Two Witches*?**

....
1 mark

(5) **a. *Two Witches* has been described as a tongue-twister. Why do you think this is?**

....

....
1 mark

b. *Two Witches* also uses word play.
   Which two words in the poem are used in word play?

....
1 mark

(6) **How are the witches from the two poems different?**

....

....
2 marks

(7) **Which poem do you prefer? Explain your answer.**

....
2 marks

....

....

Total
out of 10

        Year 4 — Targeted Comprehension

Swim, Bike, Run: Our Triathlon Story

Alistair and Jonathan (Jonny) Brownlee are brothers who were born in Yorkshire. They compete in triathlons — races that involve swimming, cycling and running. This extract from the Brownlees' autobiography is about the morning of the 2012 London Olympics triathlon final.

ALISTAIR BROWNLEE

Six forty-five a.m., 7 August 2012. I opened my eyes and looked around.

I saw the ceiling of my hotel room. I saw piles of kit strewn around the floor. I sat up in bed and asked myself how I felt.

5 How do you sleep the night before a home Olympic final, the biggest two hours of your life?

If you're me, the answer – rather unusually – was extremely well.

Two nights earlier I just couldn't get down. I had turned the light off, lain there for half an hour, turned it back on again to read, and then repeated the whole cycle. But with the hooter in London's Hyde Park just hours away, I had no such problems, nodding off around ten p.m. and then waking

10 up nine hours later, completely naturally. I had only one thought: where did the time go?

Instantly I felt the excitement. Never before have I felt like that on the morning of a race; usually there are nerves. You are shaky, you struggle to eat breakfast. This morning there was none of that. It was pure excitement.

JONNY BROWNLEE

15 With an hour and a half before the start we strolled across into Hyde Park and into the athletes' entrance, completely at ease, completely unaware of the madness that was going on everywhere else.

[...]

As we set up our helmets and running shoes in the transition area* – which we would later come

20 sprinting into after the swim and then the cycle – we became aware of the thousands crammed in along the banks of the Serpentine*. Then, coming round a corner and out from behind a screen as we headed out on our bikes for a brief warm-up, the noise hit us.

25 Bang! It was incredible, almost disconcerting*. What should we do – wave? Smile? Try to acknowledge it all?

At a stroke any final nerves went. I looked at the endless smiling faces, felt the cheers hammering my ears and thought: this is the coolest thing I've ever experienced.

An extract from *Swim, Bike, Run: Our Triathlon Story* by Alistair and Jonathan Brownlee.

Glossary

transition area — where triathletes change between sports

Serpentine — a lake in Hyde Park   disconcerting — unsettling

1 Which phrase in lines 1-6 shows that the Olympic final was very important to Alistair?

....

1 mark

2 Why do you think Alistair was surprised to have slept well?

....

....

2 marks

3 How did Alistair feel before the Olympic final?
How does this compare to the way he usually feels before a race?

....

....

2 marks

4 Why does Jonny use an exclamation mark in line 25?

....

1 mark

5 Why do you think Jonny stopped being nervous (line 27)?

....

....

1 mark

6 Write down one feature of this text which shows that it is an autobiography.

....

....

1 mark

7 How do you think you would feel if you were about to represent
your country in your favourite sport? Explain your answer.

....

2 marks

....

Total
out of 10

....

The Mysterious Parcel

By now, you've had plenty of practice at reading texts and answering questions. Now it's time to write your own text, think of some questions, and then swap with a friend.

Imagine finding a mysterious parcel in your kitchen. Write a diary entry about your feelings as you open it, and what you find inside. We've made a start, but what happens next is up to you!

Dear Diary,

The strangest thing happened today. I came downstairs to find a mysterious parcel waiting for me on the kitchen table.

E4CW21